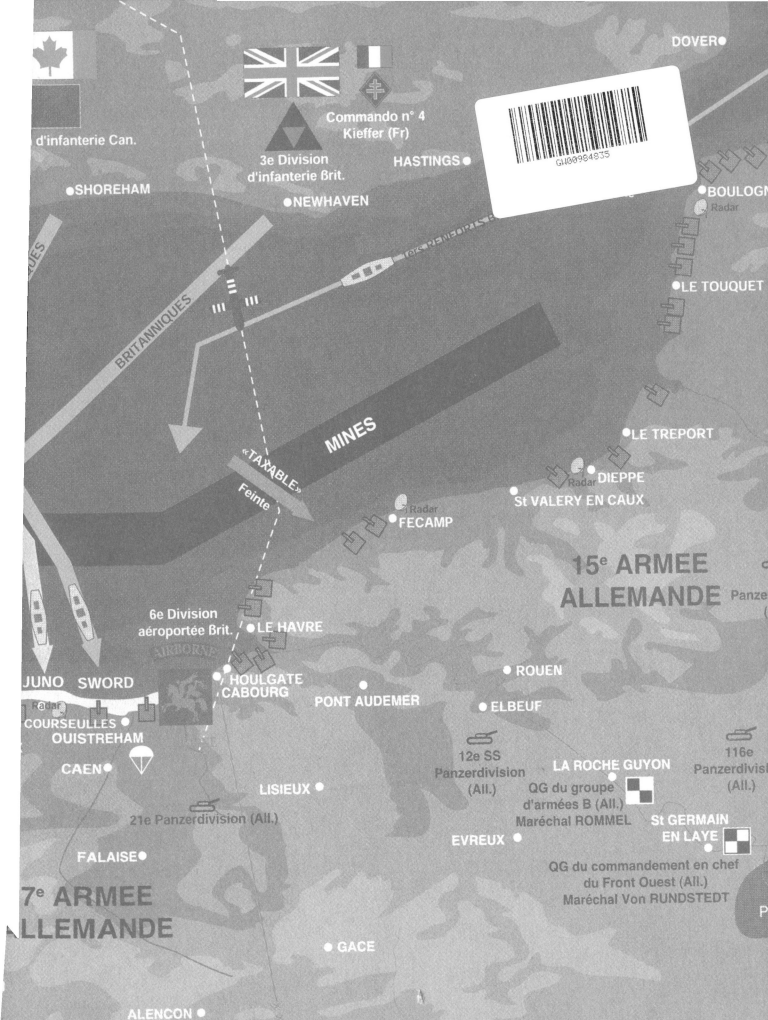

NORMANDY JUNE 44

OMAHA BEACH
POINTE DU HOC

SCRIPT: **JEAN-BLAISE DJIAN**
AND **JÉROME FÉLIX**
DRAWING: **ALAIN PAILLOU**
COLOURS: **CATHERINE MOREAU**
DOSSIER: **ISABELLE BOURNIER**
AND **MARC POTTIER**

 OREP EDITIONS

We would like to thank Pierre-Louis Gosselin
of the BIG RED ONE ASSAULT MUSEUM in
Colleville sur Mer as well as Vincent Hautin for
their technical collaboration
on this comic strip book

First published in France in December 2008 - Legal deposit: 3rd quarter 2016
ISBN 978-2-8151-0329-9

EUROPE HAD BEEN LIVING HELL UNDER NAZI OPPRESSION FOR NEARLY FIVE YEARS WHEN, ONE APRIL DAY IN LONDON...

YOU DO BEAUTIFUL WORK.

THANKS.

I IMAGINE YOU MUST BE QUITE FAMOUS BACK IN THE STATES.

QUITE THE OPPOSITE, SIR.

MAJOR TREVOR LESTER FROM THE ROYAL ARMY MEDICAL CORPS.

PETER MACTAVISH. SKETCH ARTIST. I VOLUNTEERED FOR THE LANDING.

MAY I ASK YOU A FAVOUR, MR. MACTAVISH?

SURE.

I LIVE IN NEWCASTLE, IN THE NORTH OF ENGLAND, AND GIVEN WHAT'S GOING ON RIGHT NOW, I'M NOT SURE I'LL EVER SEE MY WIFE AGAIN.

IF ANYTHING SHOULD HAPPEN, I WOULD LIKE TO SEND HER A MEMENTO OF US.

I HAVE A PHOTOGRAPH OF HER. COULD YOU DRAW BOTH OF US, CHEEK TO CHEEK, AS IF WE WERE TOGETHER? I WILL PAY ANY PRICE.

1

THIS IS WONDERFUL. YOU ARE A GREAT ARTIST, MR. MACTAVISH.

THANK YOU.

HOW MUCH DO I OWE YOU?

FORGET IT. IT WAS A PLEASURE AND...

GIVEN WHAT AWAITS US, I THINK IT'S BEAUTIFUL TO SEND A LAST MESSAGE TO THE WOMAN YOU LOVE.

THIS IS QUITE EM-BARRASS-ING...

I CANNOT LET YOU GO LIKE THIS. AT LEAST LET ME BUY YOU A BEER.

I IMAGINE YOU MUST HAVE LEFT THE COMFORT OF A NICE HOME FOR...

NOT REALLY. MY PARENTS, ESPECIALLY MY FATHER WHO USED TO BE A HIGH RANKING OFFICER, ALWAYS CALLED ME A GOOD FOR NOTHING.

THE THREE MONKEYS

I THOUGHT I COULD MAKE IT IN NEW YORK. I LEFT HOME TO ESCAPE THEIR CRITICISM AND THE CONSTANT COM-PARISON WITH MY BROTHER, JIM, THE SUCCESSFUL ONE.

LAST YEAR, HE EVEN MADE IT INTO THE HEADLINES ACROSS THE COUNTRY...

YOU WERE SAYING YOU WENT TO NEW YORK?

YEAH. AND THERE I MET GLENDA, A SWELL GIRL...

MY PARENTS DON'T APPROVE OF HER AT ALL. SHE GREW UP IN A POOR FAMILY...

2

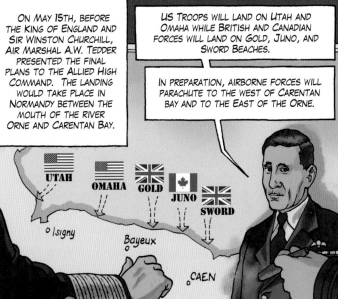

TWO WEEKS BEFORE D-DAY, MORE THAN 1.5 MILLION SOLDIERS WERE LOCKED UP IN CAMPS CALLED 'SAUSAGE CAMPS.' IT WAS THERE THE MEN LEARNED THAT THE LANDING WOULD TAKE PLACE IN NORMANDY.

OPERATION FORTITUDE WAS A DECOY OPERATION TO SPREAD THE IDEA THAT THE LANDINGS WOULD TAKE PLACE IN THE PAS DE CALAIS.

WITH THIS NEW KNOWLEDGE, NO ONE WAS ALLOWED TO LEAVE CAMP. THE GUARDS, WHO WERE NOT IN THE KNOW, HAD ORDERS TO FIRE UPON ANYONE TRYING TO VIOLATE THIS ORDER.

INSIDE CAMP WEYMOUTH, THE MOOD WAS HEAVY AND TENSE. EVERYBODY KNEW THAT TRAINING, WHICH FOR SOME HAD BEEN GOING ON FOR YEARS, WAS OVER. MANY MEN WOULD LOSE THEIR LIVES.

GLENDA DARLING, YOU HAVEN'T ANSWERED MY LAST LETTER. I THINK OF YOU ALWAYS. THE DAY OF DAYS IS APPROACHING. THIS LETTER WON'T BE SENT UNTIL AFTER THE LANDING, BUT I WANTED YOU TO KNOW HOW MUCH I LOVE YOU...

MY SKETCHES WILL BECOME PROPAGANDA POSTERS AND WILL SURELY BE PUBLISHED IN MAGAZINES. I HOPE MY FATHER WILL BE PROUD OF ME FOR ONCE.

YOU WILL SEE THAT EVERYTHING IS GOING TO BE JUST SWELL FOR US. I WANTED TO KEEP IT A SURPRISE, BUT MR. SPENCER PROMISED TO HIRE ME AT HIS ADVERTISING AGENCY WITH A GOOD SALARY WHEN I GET BACK.

HERE, SERGEANT.

ANOTHER ONE! I TOLD YOU MACTAVISH; YOUR LETTERS WON'T BE SENT UNTIL AFTER THE OPERATION...

... ??!

JIM?! YOU... YOU'RE IN THIS CAMP, TOO?

HEY BROTHER!

4

6

I HEARD THAT YOU'D VOLUNTEERED WHEN I WAS HOME IN MARCH. I HOPE YOU REALLY THOUGHT THROUGH THIS THING. IT'S GOING TO BE A BLOODY BATTLE...

YOU'RE NOT CUT OUT FOR THIS...

COME ON. LET'S GO GET A COLD BEER.

SO, YOU'RE GONNA BE LIKE ROBERT CAPA BUT WITH A CHARCOAL PENCIL? WHAT UNIT ARE YOU WITH?

I'LL BE WITH THE 1ST DIVISION, 5TH ARMY CORPS.

THE FAMOUS BIG RED ONE!

THEY'RE THE ONES THAT FOUGHT IN NORTH AFRICA AND SICILY... THEIR OBJECTIVE IS OMAHA BEACH, RIGHT?

AND YOU ?

I'M WITH THE 2ND BATTALION OF THE RANGERS. WE'VE BEEN TRAINING FOR TWO YEARS NOW. OUR TARGET IS GONNA BE THE CLIFF AT POINTE DU HOC. WE HAVE TO PREVENT ANY ATTACK ON OUR SHIPS BY NEUTRALIZING THE SIX BIG CANNONS AT THE TOP.

HOW HAVE THE FOLKS BEEN?

THEY'RE DOING ALL RIGHT, BUT I WASN'T REALLY AT HOME... I HAD TO DO SOME STUFF IN NEW YORK...

OH YEAH? LIKE WHAT?

THE NEWSPAPERS WROTE ABOUT ME LAST YEAR. I'VE BECOME SOME SORT OF SYMBOL FOR OUR TROOPS. THOUSANDS OF READERS HAD WRITTEN TO ME FOR AN UPDATE...

SO I WENT THERE...DID A FEW PRESS CONFERENCES... TO RAISE THE MORALE OF THE SOLDIERS' FAMILIES, YOU KNOW.

5

ON JUNE 2ND, SEVERAL PLANES TOOK OFF FROM THE THORNEY ISLAND AIRFIELD.

THEIR MISSION: NEUTRALIZE GERMAN RADAR AND RADIO STATIONS.

THE ATTACKS AND BROADCASTS BY RADIO LONDON ALLOWED THE GERMANS TO KNOW THAT D-DAY WAS COMING SOON.

FIELD MARSHAL ROMMEL, GREAT STRATEGIST AND MASTERMIND BEHIND THE "ATLANTIC WALL," WARNED HIS OFFICERS...

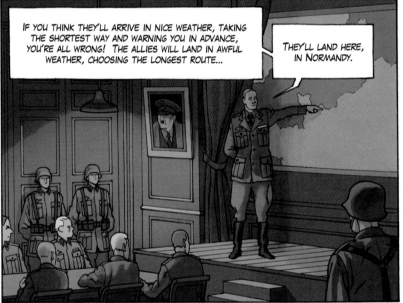

IF YOU THINK THEY'LL ARRIVE IN NICE WEATHER, TAKING THE SHORTEST WAY AND WARNING YOU IN ADVANCE, YOU'RE ALL WRONG! THE ALLIES WILL LAND IN AWFUL WEATHER, CHOOSING THE LONGEST ROUTE...

THEY'LL LAND HERE, IN NORMANDY.

INDEED, ON THE NIGHT OF THE 4TH AND 5TH OF JUNE, A FORMIDABLE ARMADA LEFT THE ENGLISH COASTS IN AWFUL WEATHER.

ALREADY THIS BAD AT 0400 HOURS...

TEDDER, OUR MEN CANNOT LAND TOMORROW. D-DAY IS GOING TO BE DELAYED ONE FULL DAY... IF THE WEATHER IMPROVES, THAT IS.

ALL CONVOYS ALREADY AT SEA MUST RETURN TO PORT.

128 SHIPS WOULD NOT RECEIVE THIS ORDER. A FLYING BOAT WAS SENT TO ORDER THEIR RETURN.

6

WEATHER SPECIALISTS ANNOUNCED A BREAK IN THE WEATHER ON THE 5TH OF JUNE. IN THE SOUTHWICK HOUSE LIBRARY, THE SUPREME HEADQUARTERS ALLIED EXPEDITIONARY FORCE DECIDED TO LAUNCH OPERATION OVERLORD THE NEXT MORNING.

AT THE NORTH WITHAM AND GREENHAM COMMON AIR FORCE BASES, AS AT ALL THE OTHERS, ANXIETY MOUNTED WHEN THE 940 PLANES TOOK OFF.

ACCORDING TO THE ORIGINAL PLAN, THE 101ST AIRBORNE DIVISION, "THE SCREAMING EAGLES," LED BY GENERAL M TAYLOR JUMPED ABOVE CARENTAN BAY TO FACILITATE THE LANDING ON UTAH BEACH.

THIS TIME AROUND, THE MACHINE WAS EN ROUTE. THERE WAS NO TURNING BACK.

MEANWHILE, CROSSING THE CHANNEL, ADMIRAL BERTRAM RAMSAY, WHO HAD ALREADY LED THE OPERATION TORCH LANDINGS, WAS LEADING A FLEET OF 6,000 SHIPS.

7

SIR TRAFFORD LEIGH-MALLORY, APPOINTED AIR COMMANDER-IN-CHIEF, WAS ASSIGNED TO BOMB THE FRENCH COASTS, INCLUDING THOSE IN THE PAS DE CALAIS TO CONTINUE DECEIVING THE GERMANS.

AT THE MOUTH OF THE ORNE AND WITH GREAT ACCURACY, THREE HORSA GLIDERS FLEW IN ABOUT 90 MEN FROM THE BRITISH 6TH AIRBORNE DIVISION UNDER THE COMMAND OF MAJOR HOWARD. THEIR EMBLEM WAS PEGASUS.

TWO OTHER GLIDERS LANDED SUCCESSFULLY NEAR THE RANVILLE BRIDGE; THE THIRD WAS LOST. THE GOAL OF THEIR OPERATION: CAPTURE AND HOLD TWO BRIDGES INTACT UNTIL RELIEVED. THE BRITISH WOULD ACHIEVE THIS AFTER ONLY 15 MINUTES AND AT THE PRICE OF 2 KILLED AND 14 INJURED SOLDIERS.

ON THE COTENTIN PENINSULA, OPERATIONS PROVED FAR MORE DIFFICULT; 2,499 SOLDIERS WERE EITHER SHOT DOWN BY THE ENEMY OR DROWNED IN THE MARSHES.

IN HIS LANDING CRAFT, PETER WAS LIVID. THE STORM WAS NOT CALMING. EXHAUSTED BY 24 HOURS WITHOUT SLEEP AND DRUGGED BY DRAMAMINE, THE SOLDIERS WERE IN BAD SHAPE.

LOST IN MEMORIES THAT COULD VERY WELL BE THEIR LAST, THE SOLDIERS WERE STOIC AND SILENT AS BOMBS FROM THE PLANES EXPLODED IN THE DISTANCE.

8

AROUND 0300 HOURS, THE SHIPS CARRYING THE 2ND BATTALION OF US RANGERS, LED BY COLONEL RUDDER, STOPPED THEIR ENGINES AT 12 NAUTICAL MILES FROM THE POINTE DU HOC.

WHY ARE WE STOPPING SO FAR OUT, CAPTAIN?

THEIR GPFS* HAVE A MAXIMUM RANGE OF 13 MILES. THEY'LL NEVER BE ABLE TO REACH US IN THIS WEATHER**.

THE SEA IS ROUGH. IT'LL TAKE HOURS FOR THE BOATS TO REACH THE COAST.

BETWEEN TWO OR THREE... IN THE MEAN TIME, THE 14-INCH CANNONS WILL COVER THEM.

BAOOM

THE THREE COMPANIES*** OF THE FIRST ASSAULT WAVE WERE ACCOMPANIED BY TWO LCAS**** CARRYING FOOD, MEDICINE, AND AMMUNITION.

YOU DON'T LOOK GOOD, JIM. FUNNY SEEING AS YOU'VE ALREADY PROVEN TO BE SO COURAGEOUS. LIKE THAT TIME WHEN...

IT'S PETER! MY BROTHER... HE VOLUNTEERED FOR THE LANDING AT OMAHA WITH THE BIG RED ONE.

SO? AND YOU'RE NOT LANDING?

FOR ME, IT'S MY JOB. BUT HIM... HE'S AN ARTIST, A DAYDREAMER. JUST CANNON FODDER...

*155MM CANNON OF FRENCH ORIGIN. **A 4 OR 5 ON THE BEAUFORT WIND FORCE SCALE. *** FOX, DOG, AND EASY. **** BRITISH LANDING CRAFT.

SERGEANT! WATER!... WE'RE TAKING ON WATER!

USE YOUR HELMETS! SCOOP IT OUT!

HO!

WHAT IS IT, CAPTAIN?

WE'VE GOT A PROBLEM. THOSE DAMNED WOODEN LCAs ARE TAKING ON WATER!

WE'RE NOT GONNA MAKE IT, CAPTAIN!

IT'S COMIN' IN TOO FAST. WE'RE GONNA SINK!

ALREADY LOST TWO BOATS AND WE'RE TAKING ON WATER TOO!

START SCOOPIN', BURKIN!

WHAT SHALL WE DO, CAPTAIN?

NOTHING. AN LCA WILL FISH THEM OUT ON THE WAY BACK.

MEANWHILE, NEAR OMAHA BEACH..

A GREAT ARTIST ONCE TOLD ME THAT IF MY DRAWINGS ARE BAD, IT'S BECAUSE I'M NOT CLOSE ENOUGH TO THE MODEL.

TODAY, I'M GONNA BE IN THE HEART OF THE ACTION.

SO IF MY SKETCHES AREN'T ANY GOOD THIS TIME AROUND, EVERYONE WHO DIDN'T BELIEVE IN ME WILL HAVE BEEN RIGHT.

AFTER SICILY AND NORTH AFRICA, LIKE MY BROTHER SAID, NOBODY IN THE BIG RED ONE HAS ANYTHING LEFT TO PROVE.

AND YET, FEW OF THEM ASKED TO GO HOME. I WONDER WHY?

WHAT'S DRIVING THEM INTO COMBAT AGAIN? ME... I'VE GOT NOTHING TO LOSE.

BUT THEM?

THEY RESPECT EACH OTHER...

...RELY ON ONE ANOTHER.

THEY IGNORE ME...

WHO CAN BLAME 'EM ?

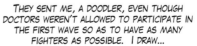

THEY SENT ME, A DOODLER, EVEN THOUGH DOCTORS WEREN'T ALLOWED TO PARTICIPATE IN THE FIRST WAVE SO AS TO HAVE AS MANY FIGHTERS AS POSSIBLE. I DRAW...

HEUU...

BLAAAHHH!

HEY! DO YOU HAVE ANY EXTRA BENZEDRINE? I LOST MINE.

DON'T TAKE THAT SHIT! IT'LL MAKE YOU DIZZY.

BETTER TO ARRIVE FRESH WHERE WE'RE HEADED... BELIEVE ME.

HUH?!!! BUT IKE* TOLD US THERE WEREN'T GOING TO BE ANY GERMANS THERE.

SURE, AND THERE ARE GORGEOUS FRENCH GIRLS WAITING FOR US ON THE BEACH.

BUT INTELLIGENCE** WAS POSITIVE: THE GERMANS GUARDING THIS BEACH WERE EITHER TOO YOUNG, TOO OLD, OR TOO INJURED TO FIGHT ON THE EASTERN FRONT.

THEY'RE PREDOMINANTLY POLISH AND RUSSIAN DRAFTEES GUARDING THIS BEACH.

THESE GUYS WERE BROUGHT HERE AGAINST THEIR WILL. DO YOU REALLY THINK THEY WOULD HAVE STAYED IN THEIR BUNKERS, WAITING TO GET KILLED?

I DON'T KNOW, BUT ONE THING'S FOR SURE...

...THIS SILENCE IS THAT OF SEASONED SOLDIERS.

THREE DAYS BEFORE D-DAY, THE 3RD REGIMENT, COMPOSED OF EXPERIENCED SOLDIERS RETURNING FROM THE EASTERN FRONT, JOINED THE FORCES ALREADY GUARDING THE COAST.

DON'T SHOOT. WAIT FOR THE RAMPS TO COME DOWN. THE GIS WILL PANIC AND JUMP IN THE WATER.

LIKE LAMBS TO THE SLAUGHTER!

ON LAND, THE CANNONS RECEIVED ORDERS TO FIRE.

* EISENHOWER: SUPREME COMMANDER OF THE ALLIED EXPEDITIONARY FORCE IN EUROPE. ** A SECRET INTELLIGENCE SERVICE

12

ALL RIGHT... HERE WE GO!

LORD, I'M GONNA BE REAL BUSY. PROBABLY WON'T HAVE ENOUGH TIME TO THINK ABOUT YOU. PLEASE DON'T FORGET ABOUT ME.

HE'S TERRIFIED. TO THINK THAT HE COULD BE AT HOME WITH HIS GIRLFRIEND!

WHY DIDN'T YOU GO BACK HOME?

YOU COULDN'T UNDERSTAND!

WHY'S THAT?

ROCKET!!!

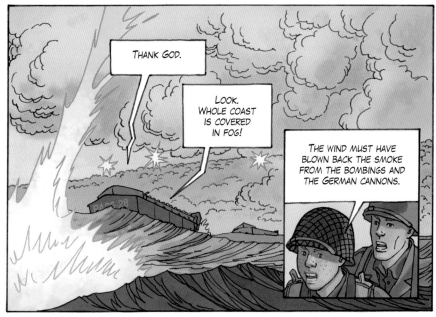

THANK GOD.

LOOK. WHOLE COAST IS COVERED IN FOG!

THE WIND MUST HAVE BLOWN BACK THE SMOKE FROM THE BOMBINGS AND THE GERMAN CANNONS.

ONCE WE'RE ON THE BEACH, WE WON'T SEE A THING. NOT EVEN WHERE THE GERMANS ARE SHOOTING FROM.

THE MEN ARE PANICKING, SERGEANT.

THEY'RE GONNA LOSE IT. YOU GOTTA REASSURE 'EM.

LISTEN UP ONE LAST TIME!

13

THE AMPHIBIOUS TANKS WERE PUT INTO WATER 4 HOURS AGO.

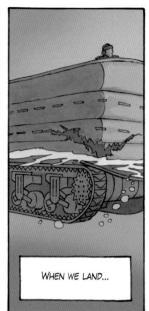

WHEN WE LAND...

...THEY'LL ALREADY BE ON THE BEACH, READY TO COVER US.

TAKE COVER BEHIND 'EM OR DIVE INTO THE SHELL CRATERS FROM EARLIER BOMBINGS. AND BELIEVE ME, THE HOLES...

...THERE'LL BE PLENTY OF 'EM...PLENTY OF 'EM...

...EVERYWHERE !

THEN RUN UP TO THE ANTI-TANK WALL AND BLOW IT TO GAIN ACCESS TO THE VALLEY. WITHOUT IT, THE VEHICLES IN THE SECOND WAVE WON'T BE ABLE TO ADVANCE INLAND.

WE'VE GOT 30 MINUTES TO DO OUR JOB. I WANT A CLEAR PATH WHEN THIS DAMNED SECOND ASSAULT WAVE HITS !

GET READY TO GO !

ARE YOU BLIND ?

WE'RE STILL ANOTHER 200 YARDS FROM THE BEACH!

THERE ARE TOO MANY SANDBARS. I CAN'T RISK GETTING STUCK IN THE SAND.

AND WITHOUT THE LCVPS, WE WON'T HAVE ANY REINFORCEMENTS.

GO!

AND JUST LIKE THAT, THE LCVP RAMPS CAME CRASHING DOWN INTO THE ICY WATER...

800 OF THE 1,000 GIs IN THE FIRST WAVE WERE KILLED OR INJURED IN LESS THAN 5 MINUTES.

IN CERTAIN COMPANIES, LOSSES REACHED 90%.

JUMP OVERBOARD!

YOUR TURN, DOODLER!

GET A MOVE ON!

HE'S TOO HEAVY! HIS ASSAULT JACKET IS DRAGGING HIM TO THE BOTTOM.

THANK GOD THEY WEREN'T ISSUED TO ARTISTS.

OPEN UP GOD DAMN IT.

COME ON!

DAMN...

15

17

SPREAD OUT! DON'T STAY TOGETHER!!!

TAKE OFF YOUR JACKETS, FELLAS! FORGET ABOUT THE GEAR.

I CAN'T!

CAN'T UNDO THESE DAMNED STRAPS!

THEY'RE TOTALLY SWOLLEN. THE STRAPS ARE TOO WET.

BECAUSE OF THE WATER SATURATION, THE 130 POUNDS OF GEAR THAT THE GIs WERE CARRYING WEIGHED MORE LIKE 220.

THEY LOOK LIKE TURTLES!

COMPLETELY EXHAUSTED, ONLY A FEW SURVIVORS REACHED THE BEACH.

SOME LITERALLY COLLAPSED FROM EXHAUSTION.

MANY WOULD NEVER GET BACK UP.

16

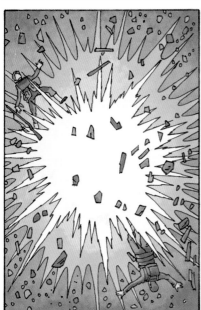

20

?!!!

WHERE ARE THE OTHER TANKS?

AT THE BOTTOM OF THE SEA...

ALMOST ALL OF THEM SANK.

HOW? HADN'T THEY BEEN TESTED?

YEAH, ON LAKES... NOT ON A SQUALLY SEA. THE FLOTATION DEVICES GAVE UP IN LESS THAN 5 MINUTES.

HEY!

WHAT SHALL WE DO?

WHERE'S THE ANTI-TANK WALL WE'RE S'POSED TO DESTROY.

DAMN IT! WE WEREN'T DEPLOYED IN THE RIGHT SPOT!

MORTAR FIRE!!!

THE KRAUTS ARE GONNA BLOW THESE ROCKS EVERYWHERE!!!

TAKE COVER!

AT THAT MOMENT, OUR SOLE PROTECTION BECAME OUR WORST ENEMY.

19

21

NEAR THE POINTE DU HOC...

...THE LCAs WERE TAKING ON WATER, SOAKING EQUIPMENT, BUT THAT WASN'T WHAT WORRIED RUDDER THE MOST...

SINCE TWO VESSELS HAD ALREADY SUNK, INSTEAD OF 225 MEN, ONLY 180 WOULD BE LANDING. AND WORSE...

TURN BACK! THE LEAD COXSWAIN MADE A MISTAKE! WE'RE NOT HEADED TOWARD THE POINTE DU HOC. THE CURRENTS ARE TAKING US TOO FAR EAST!

WHAT A DISASTER! THE ATTACK PLAN IS ALL MESSED UP.

INSTEAD OF HAVING TWO COMPANIES LANDING ON ONE SIDE OF THE CLIFF AND THE THIRD ON THE OTHER, WE'RE ALL GONNA LAND ON THE EAST SIDE.

WITH THIS DELAY, WE'RE NOT GONNA BE ABLE TO TAKE THE CLIFF BY 0700 HOURS. THEY WON'T SEND REINFORCEMENTS UNTIL WE CAN LIGHT UP THAT FLARE.

0710 HOURS

200 GERMAN GUNNERS WERE THERE TO WELCOME THE US RANGERS. DESPITE THEIR SKILL, AND EX-HAUSTED FROM A SLEEPLESS NIGHT, THE MEN WERE OVERWHELMED.

RUDDER STILL HASN'T SET OFF THE FLARE. THE OPERATION IS A FIASCO! WE'RE GONNA HAVE TO SEND IN THE 500 RANGERS WHO WERE SUPPOSED TO HELP OUT AT OMAHA.

* DUKWS: AN AMERICAN AMPHIBIOUS TRUCK DESIGNED BY GMC, FIXED WITH A BORROWED LADDER FROM THE LONDON FIRE DEPARTMENT. AT THE TOP OF THE LADDER WAS A BRITISH DOUBLE MACHINE-GUN.

THE GERMAN SOLDIERS FOUND IT DIFFICULT TO FALL BACK SINCE THE GROUND ATOP THE CLIFF HAD BEEN SO HEAVILY BOMBED.

THEY'RE ATTACKING FROM THE TRENCHES.

FIVE MINUTES HERE, THEN THEY'LL DISAPPEAR AND REAPPEAR WHERE WE WON'T HEAR THEM...

THIS COULD GET ROUGH... HANG IN THERE, FELLAS!

RUDDER HERE. THE HOC IS ALMOST SECURED... HEAVY LOSSES... NEED REINFORCEMENTS IMMEDIATELY...

GOOD WORK... NEGATIVE ON THE REINFORCEMENTS. THEY'RE ALREADY AT OMAHA.

ONE HOUR LATER...

HEY!

WHAT IS IT, SERGEANT?

WE LOST ABOUT 60 MEN* FOR NOTHING. LOOK, CAPTAIN.

OUT OF THE SIX FAMOUS CANNONS AT POINTE DU HOC THAT WE WERE SUPPOSED TO DESTROY, FIVE OF THEM ARE DAMNED TELEPHONE POLES! AND THE OTHER ONE** WAS ALREADY TAKEN CARE OF...

WE TRAINED TO CLIMB CLIFFS FOR THE LAST SIX MONTHS FOR TELEPHONE POLES! WE CLIMBED UP THIS THING FOR NOTHING!

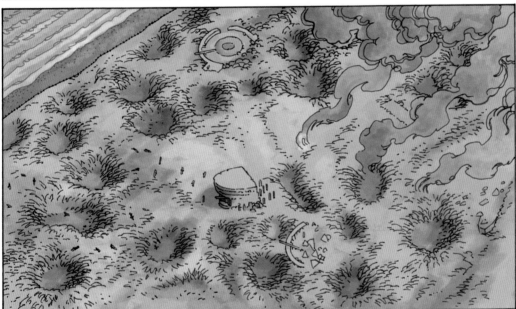

IT'S A **22** MILLIMETRE CANNON...

WE'D BETTER GET GOING ON OUR SECOND MISSION : TAKE CONTROL OF THE COASTAL HIGHWAY AND THE INTERSECTION TO KEEP THE GERMANS FROM SENDING REINFORCEMENTS TO OMAHA BEACH !

* TWO-THIRDS INJURED, ONE-THIRD DEAD.   **THIS CANNON HAD BEEN DESTROYED IN A BOMBING TWO WEEKS EARLIER.

DURING THIS TIME ON OMAHA BEACH...

HELP! HE.. HELP ME.

WE'RE ALL GONNA DIE !

STAY STRONG. THE SECOND ASSAULT WAVE 'S GONNA BE HERE IN 20 MINUTES !

STRANGELY, IT WAS IN THE MIDDLE OF THIS HELL THAT I REMEMBERED WHY I WAS THERE.

ALL AROUND ME, THE ZEAL FOR COMBAT HAD BEEN REPLACED BY A STATE OF LIFELESSNESS.

NOBODY MOVED A MUSCLE.

AND SOME WHO HAD TAKEN TOO MUCH DRAMAMINE EVEN FELL ASLEEP.

EVERYBODY WAS TENSE, EDGY...

I HELD ON TO MY DRAWING.

SUDDENLY, AND IN A STATE OF TOTAL MADNESS*, SOME GIs BEGAN GETTING UP AND WALKING AROUND IN A TRANCE AS IF NOTHING WAS HAPPENING. THESE MEN BECAME EASY TARGETS.

MEANWHILE, THE TIDE WAS COMING IN.

KI... KILL ME !

DON'T LET ME DIE LIKE THIS !

IF ONLY HE KNEW THAT I DON'T EVEN HAVE A GUN !...

*SEVERAL SOLDIERS ON THE BEACH SUFFERED FROM HALLUCINATIONS; FIRING IN EVERY DIRECTION AROUND THEM, INCLUDING AT THEIR FELLOW SOLDIERS.

EVERYTHING AROUND ME WAS EXPLODING. I FELT LIKE I WAS HIDING BEHIND MY SKETCHPAD AND PENCILS...

NO!

?!!!

REINFORCEMENTS ARE HERE!

THE SECOND ASSAULT WAVE ARRIVED AS PLANNED 30 MINUTES AFTER THE FIRST. AND UNFORTUNATELY, THE TIDE HAD COME IN JUST ENOUGH TO COVER THE BEACH'S OBSTACLES.

BY CHANCE, SOME LCVPs MANAGED TO MAKE IT THROUGH THE MINES.

BUT SINCE NOBODY TOLD THE GIs TO TAKE OFF THEIR ASSAULT JACKETS...

...THE SECOND WAVE PASSED MUCH LIKE THE FIRST.

...AN ABSOLUTE DISASTER.

THE FEW SURVIVORS SCATTERED THEMSELVES OUT ALL ALONG THE BEACH, EXACTLY LIKE THE FIRST WAVE HAD DONE ONLY 30 MINUTES EARLIER.

I'VE GOT THE BANGALORE*!

SOMEBODY KNOW HOW TO USE THESE THINGS?

OVER HERE!

YOU A COMBAT ENGINEER, SERGEANT?

NO, BUT I'VE USED THIS KIND OF THING ALREADY IN SICILY.

TAKE COVER!

IT'S GONNA BLOW!

*THE BANGALORE TORPEDO WAS AN EXPLOSIVE DEVICE USED TO DEMOLISH BARBED WIRE FENCING.

28

SERGEANT, THE GERMANS ARE SNIPING US FROM THE BUNKERS OVER ON THE LEFT.

BUT IF WE CAN MAKE IT TO THE BOTTOM OF THAT HILL, WE'LL BE OUT OF THEIR FIELD OF VISION.

RUN ALL THE WAY TO THE CLIFF, SERGEANT?

THERE'S NO COVER. IT'S WIDE OPEN!

THE KRAUTS'LL SHOOT AT US LIKE WE'RE RABBITS.

TWO KINDS OF PEOPLE ARE GOING TO STAY ON THIS BEACH...

I'M SAYIN' WE'VE GOTTA TRY OUR LUCK.

THE VILLA IN RUINS! HE MADE IT!

THAT'S MORE THAN HALF THE WAY THERE.

TATATATA

THE DEAD AND THOSE WHO ARE ABOUT TO DIE.

GET ALL THE BOYS TOGETHER. WE'VE GOTTA JOIN HIM!

AT 0710 HOURS, 23 GIs MADE A RUN FOR IT IN AN OPERATION INSPIRED BY UTTER DESPERATION.

29

BARELY HALF OF THE MEN WOULD REACH THE VILLA IN RUINS.

CAREFUL BOYS. LOOKS LIKE THERE'S A MINE FIELD BETWEEN US AND THAT CLIFF.

IF THE GERMANS MINED THIS AREA, SARGE...

IT'S 'CAUSE THEY KNOW THIS POSITION IS VULNERABLE. WE'VE GOTTA GIVE IT A GO.

MINEN
Terrain Miné

THIS TIME, I'M GOING FIRST!

OK. FIND US A PASSAGEWAY.

TAKE COVER IN THE GRASS! THE KRAUTS WON'T BE ABLE TO KEEP YOU IN THEIR SIGHTS!

ATATATAT

PLAOUF

SLOW AND STEADY.

WELL... NOT THAT WAY.

HUH???

THE GRASS IS PARTED 'CAUSE SOMEONE ALREADY CAME THROUGH!

THERE'S A TRAIL!

GOD IS WITH US, BOYS! GO!

28

30

CRAWLING FOR THEIR LIVES, THE 13 REMAINING GIs MADE IT TO THE BASE OF THE CLIFF UNSCATHED.

NOW WE SHOULD BE ABLE TO CLIMB UP THERE WITHOUT A PROBLEM.

STAY IN SINGLE FILE AND MOVE QUICKLY!

WAIT A MOMENT LONGER... THERE...

FIRE!

TA TATA TA

BATTLE-HARDENED BY COMBAT IN SICILY AND NORTH AFRICA, THE SERGEANT DOES NOT PANIC...

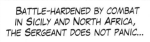

SMOKE GRENADES! SPREAD OUT!

ATTACK FROM ALL SIDES!

THERE!

AND THERE!

EVERY GUY OUT HERE WAS BROUGHT UP BY THEIR PARENTS TO BE NICE BOYS.

TOM WAS A FLORIST. HERBERT WAS A BAKER...

NOTHING BUT A BUNCH OF WILLING GUYS WHO WERE THROWN INTO COMBAT AND ASKED TO BECOME PROFESSIONAL KILLERS. AND THAT'S EXACTLY WHAT THEY ARE NOW!

SO IF YOU WANT TO SURVIVE IN THIS HELL, GRAB A GUN...

...AND USE IT.

IF NOT... JUST STAY HERE...

... AND HIDE!!

OH NO!

GERMANS ARE GOING TO AMBUSH THEM!

THEY'LL BE SLAUGHTERED...

3₁

BY GRENADES,

GUNS,

OR HAND-TO-HAND COMBAT,

WE ATTACKED THE GERMANS...

I LIKE ALL THE OTHERS.

AT THAT SAME MOMENT, THE SITUATION HAD BECOME CRITICAL.

HURRY AND BLOW UP THESE GOD DAMNED HEDGEHOGS!

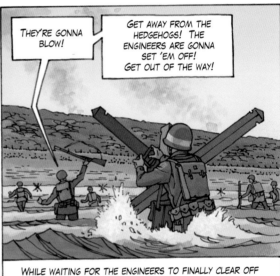

THEY'RE GONNA BLOW!

GET AWAY FROM THE HEDGEHOGS! THE ENGINEERS ARE GONNA SET 'EM OFF! GET OUT OF THE WAY!

WHILE WAITING FOR THE ENGINEERS TO FINALLY CLEAR OFF PARTS OF THE BEACH, THE MAJOR GENERAL GAVE THE ORDER TO STOP DEBARKING ALL VEHICLES.

THIS LEFT ABOUT TWENTY TRANSPORTERS CIRCLING IN THE CHANNEL. WITH LITTLE FUEL, THE VESSELS WOULD SINK IF IT TOOK TOO LONG TO SECURE PATHS TO THE BEACH.

SOLDIERS CONTINUED DEPLOYMENT AT 140 YARDS FROM THE BEACH...

OUR MISSION IS TO PROTECT THE OMAHA'S RIGHT FLANK. WE'VE GOTTA HEAD TO THE ROAD, BACK THERE, AND SET UP A ROAD BLOCK...

WHERE THIS 20 MILLIMETRE CANNON CAN'T HIT US.

POINTE DU HOC

WHY AT THIS INTERSECTION, LIEUTENANT?

THAT'S WHERE WE'RE GOING TO MEET UP WITH THE 116TH INFANTRY REGIMENT OF THE 29TH DIVISION TO MARCH TOGETHER TO ISIGNY.

LET'S HEAD ON OUT, BOYS!

GOOD. NOW THAT WE'VE ESTABLISHED OUR DEFENSIVE POSITION, WE'VE GOT TO KEEP CONTACT WITH THE ENEMY. WE'VE GOTTA KNOW WHERE HE IS, REMIND HIM THAT WE'RE HERE...

AND KEEP HIM FROM ORGANIZING ANY KIND OF COUNTERATTACK.

JACK, PACO, AND STEVE, FORM PATROLS OF A DOZEN MEN AND GO LEAPFROGGING SOUTH OF THE ROAD!

WE'VE ALSO GOT TO FIGURE OUT WHERE THEY'RE HIDING THOSE FAMOUS CANNONS!

HEY JACK, YOU SEE THOSE TRACKS IN THE FIELD? WEIRD, HUH?

YEAH. LET'S FOLLOW THEM.

$\frac{3}{4}$

STAFF SERGEANT JACK KUHN AND FIRST SERGEANT LEN LOMELL WERE HARDLY COMFORTED BY WHAT THEY SAW.

MY GOD! HERE ARE THE CANNONS !!

STAND READY. WE ATTACK IN 15 MINUTES.

HO. THE ENEMY !

REINFORCEMENTS WILL ARRIVE IN NO TIME... WE MUST REGAIN CONTROL OF THE ROAD AT ALL COST ! WE HAVE AT LEAST 50 MEN AND THE ELEMENT OF SURPRISE...

THEY AREN'T WATCHING THE CANNONS*. WE'VE GOTTA DESTROY THEM...

OK, BUT WE'VE GOT TO DO IT WITHOUT THEM NOTICING.

WE'VE EACH GOT A THERMITE GRENADE**...

* THE IRONY OF THIS STORY IS THAT THE GERMANS NEVER RECEIVED ORDERS TO USE THE CANNONS. AND YET, THEY WOULD HAVE BEEN ABLE TO FIRE UPON BOTH UTAH AND OMAHA BEACHES FROM POINTE DU HOC. ** THERMITE GRENADES DO NOT EXPLODE. HEATING UP TO TEMPERATURES OF 3000ºC, THEY BURN HOT ENOUGH TO MELT METAL.

FOR THEIR HEROIC ACTIONS, SERGEANTS KUHN AND LOMELL WERE DECORATED WITH THE DISTINGUISHED SERVICE CROSS AFTER THE WAR HAD ENDED.

DURING THAT TIME AT OMAHA, THE SITUATION HAD NOT YET IMPROVED. THE LCTS WERE STILL TURNING IN CIRCLES OFF SHORE WHILE THE GIS FOUGHT DESPERATELY TO SURVIVE AGAINST GERMAN GUNFIRE.

JUMP IN THE WATER!

LUCKILY, THESE GIS AND THOSE OF THE SUBSEQUENT WAVES DIDN'T HAVE THE ASSAULT JACKETS* WITH THE DEFECTIVE STRAPS.

CLICK

SURVIVORS CONTINUED TO GATHER ALONG THE EMBANKMENT. WITH MIXED COMPANIES, INEXISTENT COMMUNICATION, SUPPLIES LOST TO THE SEA... HOPELESS CONFUSION WOULD SOON COME CRASHING DOWN UPON THE BEACH. ALL IS LOST!

FACED WITH SUCH A DISASTER, LIEUTENANT GENERAL BRADLEY WAS FORCED TO MAKE A HEARTBREAKING DECISION.

STOP THE DEPLOYMENT OF REIN-FORCEMENTS.

ABANDON OMAHA?!! WHAT ABOUT OUR BOYS? THEY'LL ALL BE STUCK THERE...

IF WE'RE GOING TO SAVE THIS OPERATION THEN WE DON'T HAVE THE CHOICE.

ORDER ALL PILOTS TO DEPLOY THE REST OF THE TROOPS ON UTAH BEACH. WE'VE TAKEN THE BEACH.

LUCKILY, THREE OTHER GROUPS OF SOLDIERS, FOLLOWING PETER'S EXAMPLE, DECIDED TO ACT RATHER THAN WAIT TO DIE.

THEIR ACTIONS WOULD CHANGE THE COURSE OF THE BATTLE.

* THE DEFECTIVE ASSAULT JACKETS WERE ONLY WORN BY THE FIRST TWO WAVES OF SOLDIERS BECAUSE NOT ENOUGH HAD BEEN MADE.

AT THAT SAME MOMENT, THE NAVAL COMMANDERS, IGNORING DIRECT ORDERS, DECIDED TO MOVE IN CLOSER TO THE BEACHES FOR A MORE PRECISE VIEW OF THEIR OBJECTIVES.

BUT CAPTAIN ?!!! WE'RE PUTTING OURSELVES IN RANGE OF THE GERMAN CANNONS !

I KNOW ! ADVANCE!

HERE AND THERE, CLEVER SOLDIERS CLEAR PATHS FOR THE LANDING CRAFT TO UNLOAD HEAVY MATERIALS...

AT THAT MOMENT, AND AFTER 2 HOURS OF UNRELENTING COMBAT...

WE'RE HOLDING POSITION, SERGEANT.

IGNITE THE RED SMOKE GRENADE.

AT 0900 HOURS, THE GIS HAD PIERCED THE FRONT AT FOUR SPOTS AND HAD TAKEN HOLD OF ONLY ONE GERMAN POSITION.

AT 0930 HOURS, THE MAJOR GENERAL CANCELLED HIS ORDERS TO ABORT DEPLOYMENT AT OMAHA. LUCKILY, THE REDEPLOYMENT OF TROOPS AT UTAH BEACH HAD YET TO COMMENCE.

BY 1030 HOURS, 2 OPENINGS ON THE BEACH HAD BEEN SECURED.

FOR AS MUCH AS HAD HAPPENED, THE BATTLE WASN'T OVER YET. THE LAST GERMAN STRONGHOLDS WOULD ONLY BE TAKEN THE NEXT DAY, FOLLOWING A DAY OF NON-STOP FIGHTING.

IN ALL, OVER 1,200 GIS* GAVE THEIR LIVES FOR VICTORY OF A MISSION THAT DIDN'T GO ACCORDING TO THE MAJOR GENERAL'S

* 1,200 DEAD, 2,682 INJURED

The crossroad at Pointe du Hoc.

THEY JUST KEEP COMIN', SARGE. WE JUST LOST ANOTHER THIRTY MEN...

AND WE'RE ALMOST OUT OF AMMO. WE CAN'T HOLD 'EM OFF MUCH LONGER.

I KNOW ALL THAT, GARETH, BUT I DON'T HAVE ANY OTHER IDEA! COMMUNICATIONS ARE DOWN. I CAN'T GET THE SHIP TO SEND REINFORCEMENTS.

WE'RE HOLDIN' ON BY A THREAD AND THE ENEMY JUST KEEPS COMING AND COMING...

THIS MAY BE THE END, BOYS.

THIS REALLY IS THE END, SARGE! THEY LAUNCH ONE MORE ATTACK AND WE'RE GONERS!

PAW PAW

PAW

TATATA

41

WHA...WHAT A MIRACLE...

BY THE GRACE OF GOD YOU GUYS SHOWED IN THE NICK OF TIME! WHERE DID YOU COME FROM?

WE GOT LOST AROUND OMAHA. I DON'T KNOW HOW WE DID IT! WE MADE IT ACROSS ENEMY LINES AND HERE WE ARE...

ON THE MORNING OF THE 7TH, THE TROOPS FROM OMAHA WERE BARELY ON THE OUTSKIRTS OF VIERVILLE AND THE RANGERS WERE STILL ALL ALONE. THEY HADN'T SLEPT FOR TWO DAYS AND NIGHTS.

COLONEL, THE SHIP HAS FINALLY RECEIVED WORD OF OUR SITUATION. THEY KNOW THAT WE DON'T HAVE ENOUGH MEN TO HOLD THE HOC AND THE ROAD...

THEY'RE ORDERING US TO LEAVE THE FRONT. WE HAVE TO LEAVE THE ROAD AND GO BACK TO SUPPORT DEFENCES ON THE CLIFF.

TELL 'EM THAT WE'VE GOT ALMOST NO AMMO, NO FOOD, AND THAT OUR INJURED ARE IN TERRIBLE CONDITION. *

TELL 'EM TO SEND REINFORCEMENTS! AND FAST!

* BETWEEN THE BATTLE AT POINTE DU HOC AND ALL OF THE COUNTERATTACKS, THE RANGERS MUST HAVE ENGAGED OVER ONE THOUSAND GERMAN SOLDIERS IN COMBAT. OF THE INITIAL 225 RANGERS, ONLY 90 WERE STILL IN CONDITION FOR COMBAT BY NIGHTFALL ON JUNE 8TH.

MARINES FROM THE USS TEXAS LAND AT POINTE DU HOC, BRINGING WITH THEM FOOD AND AMMUNITION.

WHOA! SHOTS ARE STILL FIRING LEFT AND RIGHT UP THERE!

YEAH. IT'S ABOUT TIME WE GOT HERE. OUR BOYS HAVE GOTTA BE IN A SORRY STATE.

TATATATATA

SOLDIERS TOO INJURED FOR BATTLE BUT STILL CAPABLE OF CLIMBING DOWN THE CLIFF MEET THE LANDING CRAFT.

BY THE EVENING OF JUNE 7TH, THE SECTOR WAS CONSIDERED NEUTRALIZED.

AT THAT MOMENT, THE 3RD BATTALION OF THE 29TH DIVISION'S 116TH INFANTRY REGIMENT, COMING FROM OMAHA, MADE THEIR WAY TOWARD THE RANGERS.

IN THE CITY OF SAINT PIERRE-DU-MONT, SITUATED LESS THAN ONE KILOMETRE FROM THE RANGERS' COMMAND POST, THE AMERICAN FORCES ADVANCE.

SEEING THE ENEMY COME FROM THIS SIDE AS WELL, THE APPREHENSIVE GERMANS DON'T DARE ATTEMPT A COUNTERATTACK...

WHICH WORKS OUT WELL BECAUSE...

ANOTHER COUNTERATTACK WILL WIPE US OUT. THE MEN ARE BEYOND EXHAUSTION, COLONEL...

ON THE MORNING OF THE 8TH, THE MAJOR GENERAL, STILL AT SEA, PRESUMES THAT THE ATTACK ON THE CLIFF HAD FAILED, ORDERING AN AIR STRIKE...

P 47 PILOTS WERE READY TO RAIN HELLFIRE UPON THE RANGERS WHEN...

HEY, FELLAS! THEY'RE OURS! THEY'RE GONNA BOMB US!!

ABORT MISSION! ALL PILOTS, REPEAT : ABORT MISSION. OUR MEN HAVE THE CLIFF! ABORT MISSION..

42

TA TA TA TA TA TA TA TA

WHAT A RELIEF! NOW THAT THEY KNOW THAT WE'VE GOT THE CLIFF... THEY'LL FINALLY SEND US REINFORCEMENTS...

NOT ANY TOO SOON, EITHER! THREE DAYS AND NIGHTS WITH-OUT SLEEP... I'M DEAD TIRED!

AT THAT MOMENT, UNITS FROM THE RANGER'S 5TH, VIRTUALLY UNSCATHED, AND THE THREE REMAINING COMPANIES OF THE 2ND BATTALION APPROACH FROM OMAHA BEACH.

HALT!

RUDDER'S RANGERS WEREN'T ABLE TO CAPTURE THE CLIFF, LISTEN!

LISTEN TO WHAT, CAPTAIN?

OUR MACHINE GUNS SHOOT BETWEEN 400 AND 600 ROUNDS A MINUTE. GERMAN GUNS ARE BETWEEN 1,200 AND 1,500. THOSE SHOTS WERE FIRED FROM A GERMAN WEAPON...

HEAD ON OUT! WE'VE GOT ANOTHER FIGHT AHEAD OF US.

PAW PAW PAW

AAAH!

WHAT THE DEVIL!!

HEY!! THOSE AREN'T GERMANS WE'RE SHOOTING AT, CAPTAIN! THOSE ARE RANGERS!!!

HOLD YOUR FIRE!

THOUGHT YOU BOYS DIDN'T MAKE IT...

EVERYBODY THOUGHT THAT. EVEN ON BOARD THE U.S.S TEXAS THEY THOUGHT THAT. YOU KILLED TWO OF MY MEN AND INJURED 6 OTHERS, CAPTAIN...

YES, IT'S HORRIBLE!

43

AND WHEN I FOUND OUT THAT ONE OF THE COLONELS WAS COMING TO THE POINTE DU HOC, I DIDN'T HESITATE A SECOND. NOT KNOWING WHETHER YOU MADE IT OR NOT WAS TOO PAINFUL.

WE BOTH MADE IT, BROTHER. AND FOR YOU THE WAR IS OVER!

I'M NOT GOING BACK JIM. I CAN'T!

I GUESS YOU'RE HEADED BACK HOME TOMORROW? WHEN YOU GET BACK, THE PAPERS ARE GOING TO GO CRAZY FOR YOUR SKETCHES.

YOU MADE IT, BRO. YOU'RE GOING TO BE A HUGE STAR!

WHAT?!!!

THE FOLKS, GLENDA... EVERYBODY'LL BE WAITING FOR GOOD OL' PETER TO COME HOME.

HE DOESN'T EXIST ANYMORE!

PETER, IF YOU WANT TO REJOIN THE BIG RED ONE, IT'S NOW OR NEVER!

PETER... NO! WAIT!!!

TAKE CARE OF YOURSELF, BROTHER.

JIM!

PETER!

HEY, GUYS!! ... MY BROTHER JUMPED ON A MINE!!! OVER HERE! HURRY! YOU GOTTA SAVE HIM!!

SORRY, SOLDIER! DON'T HAVE THE TIME! WE'VE ALREADY GOT PLENTY OF WORK!!

HANG IN THERE, JIM! I KNOW AN ENGLISH DOCTOR! I'M GONNA CALL HIM! IT'S GONNA BE OK, JIM! EVERYTHING'S GONNA BE JUST FINE!!

ROGUE TO 30TH BRITISH CORPS, ROGUE TO 30TH BRITISH CORPS, OVER.

ROGUE, 30TH BRITISH CORPS HERE. WHAT'S YOUR REQUEST? OVER.

4 5

THE END

NORMANDY JUNE 44

A DOSSIER FROM **ISABELLE BOURNIER** AND **MARC POTTIER**

Soldiers, Sailors and Airmen of the Allied Expeditionary Force!
You are about to embark upon the Great Crusade, toward which we have striven these many months. The eyes of the world
are upon you. The hopes and prayers of liberty-loving people everywhere march with you. In company with our brave Allies
and brothers-in-arms on other Fronts, you will bring about the destruction of the German war machine, the elimination of
Nazi tyranny over the oppressed peoples of Europe, and security for ourselves in a free world. […] I have full confidence in
your courage and devotion to duty and skill in battle. We will accept nothing less than full Victory!
Good luck! And let us beseech the blessing of Almighty God upon this great
and noble undertaking.

The D-Day Statement from General Dwight D. Eisenhower, Supreme Commander of the Allied Expeditionary Force,
distributed to all the members of the expeditionary force on the eve of the invasion.

OPERATION *Overlord*

It was at the Casablanca Conference, in January 1943, when Roosevelt and Churchill made the decision to attack the Reich by launching a vast landing operation on the European continent. The Combined Chiefs of Staff created COSSAC, an Anglo-American planning staff of thousands of strategists, to plan one of the largest military operations of the 20th Century.

Why Normandy?

The Combined Chiefs of Staff needed first to determine an assault sector. While the Pas de Calais, with its proximity to Great Britain, seemed like a favourable landing site, the coastal defences of the Atlantic Wall were far too strong. The coast of Normandy, however, presented different advantages: long, sandy beaches shielded from strong winds by the Cotentin peninsula, deep-water ports like that of Cherbourg to the West and Le Havre to the East, a coast with lightly-fortified defences, and the possibility to cut off the coastal highway to prevent any German reinforcements from a counterattack. After much deliberation, it was decided in July of 1943 that the landings would take place on the 1st of May, 1944, in the Bay of the Seine, on three beaches: two British and one American (the future

Omaha being code named Beach 313). In early 1944, Eisenhower and Montgomery decided to expand the landing to five beaches.

Requiring additional preparations, the launching of the bridgehead would be delayed by one month from the original landing date.

Aerial bombardments were launched to cut off enemy lines of communication.

Officers from the 6th British Airborne Division synchronize their watches before taking off for Normandy.

ring the large June 6th anniversary ceremonies (the 40th, 50th, or 60th anniversary), where the commemorations at this site carry special symbolism among the grandeur and majesty of the cemetery.

"Liberty road, stone markers strech from Normandy to Bastogne, Belgium, along the route of the liberating American Army"

Saving the Pointe du Hoc

The Pointe du Hoc remains one of the most famous places of the Battle of Normandy. In this memorial, also entrusted to the American Battle Monuments Commission, everything was left untouched, just as it was following combat. Bomb craters and shrapnel, eviscerated bunkers and barbed wire attest to the barrage of gunfire and the violent combat. Walking about this lunar terrain atop the cliff that

Colonel Rudder's men climbed allow to better understand the heroic feat of the Rangers.

But nature and the waves erode the cliff. In only sixty years, the Pointe du Hoc had receded nearly 10 metres. The German command post is threatened with collapsing. Is it imaginable to watch such a historical place progressively disappear?

American and French authorities decided to react. Experts from the University of Texas, the university where Colonel Rudder became president after the war, studied the situation and proposed pouring concrete in the cavities at the foot of the cliff to prevent erosion. The cost would be rather expensive, but it is necessary to save such a symbolic site of American combat.

R. de Lue's statue was erected in honor of the glory of the American youth.

The Pointe du Hoc's ground was cratered and demolished by the intensity of the combat.

15

D-DAY
Books, Films, and Music

For Reading Pleasure...

Ambrose, Stephen E. : D-Day June 6, 1944 : the battle for the Normandy Beaches, Paperback, 2002.
Ambrose, Stephen E. : Band of Brothers, Paperback, 2001.
Bevor, Antony : D-Day : from the beaches to Paris, Hardcover, 2009.
Desquesnes, Rémy : Normandy 44, Rennes, Ouest-France, 2009.
Holmes, Richard : The D-day experience from invasion to liberation, Hardcover, 2004)
Whelan, Richard and Robert Capa : Robert Capa, the definitive collection, Phaidon Press, 2004.

For viewing pleasure...

Apocalypse, Henri de Turenne, Louis Costelle, Jean-Louis Guillaud, 2009 (documentary of HD color images).
D-Day in colour, 2004.
Jour J – Battle of Normandy, 2004 (documentary).
Saving Private Ryan, Steven Spielberg, 1998 (fiction).
The Big Red one, Samuel Fuller, 1980 (fiction).
The longest Day, Andrew Marton, 1962 (fiction).

For listening pleasure...

Victory Concert – Echoes of 1944, Claude Bolling big band.
The Essential Glenn Miller (3 CD), Glenn Miller orchestra.
Complete prestige Carnegie Hall 1943-1944, Duke Ellington.
D-Day and the battle of Normandy 1944 by Various artists.

Thanks to Rémy Desquesnes, historian, for his proofreading and advice.

101e Division aéroportée US

1e Division d'infanterie US
PORTLAND
WEYMOUTH

US

US

S.H.A.E.
Grand quartier
des force
expeditionna
alliées

3

50e Division d'infanterie Brit.

SOUTHAMPTON ●

PORTSMOUTH ●

I. OF WIGHT

CANADIENS

BRITANNIQUES

ZONE
"Z"

«BIG DRUM»

Feinte

Radar

CHERBOURG

Radar

AIRBORNE
AA

82e Division aéroportée US

Ste MERE EGLISE

UTAH

OMAHA

G

Radar

Pte du HOC

ARROMANC

CARENTAN

BA

AIRBORNE

101e Division aéroportée US

St LÔ

QG du 84e corps d'armée (All.)
Général MARCKS

VIRE

Radar

AVRANCHES

MORT

St MALO

DINAN ●